BOOK REPORT BACKPACK

INSTANT IDEAS
FOR CREATIVE
BOOK REPORTS

GRADES 4–8

WRITTEN BY LINDA SPELLMAN
ILLUSTRATED BY BEV ARMSTRONG

THE LEARNING WORKS

TABLE OF CONTENTS

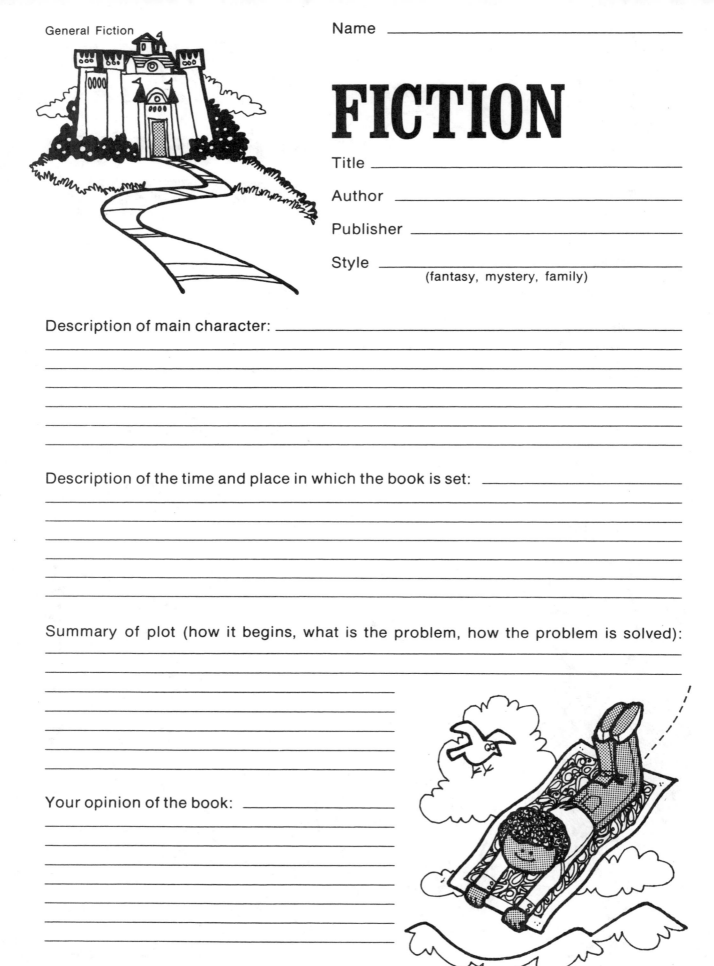

Name _____

FICTION

Title _____

Author _____

Publisher _____

Style _____
(fantasy, mystery, family)

Description of main character: _____
_____
_____
_____
_____
_____
_____

Description of the time and place in which the book is set: _____
_____
_____
_____
_____
_____
_____

Summary of plot (how it begins, what is the problem, how the problem is solved):
_____
_____
_____
_____
_____

Your opinion of the book: _____
_____
_____
_____
_____
_____
_____

Name _____

COME TO THE CIRCUS

★ STARRING ★

_____
Book title

Written by

_____

The Big Top setting of this story:

_____
_____
_____
_____
_____
_____
_____

The main character is . . .

_____
_____
_____
_____
_____
_____
_____
_____

And the best part is:

_____
_____
_____
_____
_____
_____
_____

Name _____

Make a **FLIP BOOK** Book Report

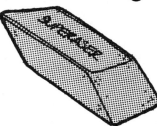

Draw pictures to illustrate your book according to the labels below each square. Cut out the squares, put into correct order, and staple to form a mini-book. You may color, if you have time.

Name _____

1. Title, author

2. The scene (setting)

3. The main character

4. A problem to solve

FLIP BOOK

5. A funny event

6. An exciting event

7. Solving the problem

8. The end

General Fiction

Name _____

THE BOOK REPORTER

VOL. XXV NO. 27 _____ , 19 __ 20¢

OUTSTANDING BOOK OFF PRESS

New Author Announced

_____
_____
_____
_____

Main Characters Described

_____
_____
_____
_____
_____
_____
_____
_____
_____
_____
_____
_____

A scene from the book that shows

_____
_____
_____

The Critic Says . . .

_____
_____
_____
_____
_____
_____
_____

Plot Revealed

_____
_____
_____
_____
_____
_____
_____
_____
_____
_____
_____
_____

Local Weather

_____
_____
_____
_____

Name _____

What if your book were made into a movie?

ROXY THEATER

NOW PLAYING: _____

BY _____

TICKETS

ILLUSTRATION OF
MAIN CHARACTER ↓

A New York film critic states that . . . . _____
_____
_____
_____
_____
_____
_____
_____
_____
_____

Summary

9

Send a picture post card. Illustrate your book on the opposite side of the paper. Write a summary in the body of your letter.

The picture on the reverse shows _____

Dear _____ ,

There is so much to tell you!

To:

Author _____

c/o
Book title _____

Publisher _____

City where published _____

Coral Reefs USA 15c

BANNER BRIGADE

Make a banner to advertise your book by following these easy directions.

You will need 2 sheets of construction paper of contrasting colors plus one piece of string approximately 30 inches long.

Use one piece of paper 12" x 18" for the main part of the banner. Leave a 1" margin top and bottom.

To make frames for the top and bottom, take one sheet of 9" x 12" paper. Cut into 2 pieces 4½" x 12" long. Fold each of these pieces twice the long way.

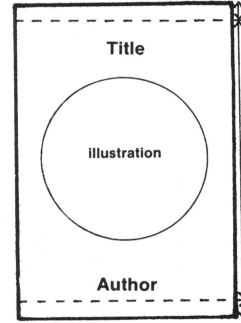

Title

illustration

Author

1"

16"

1"

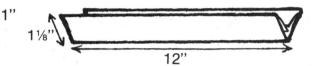

1⅛"

12"

Set up your paper as shown. Color in and frame.

Place string along the inside fold of one frame. Then staple frame over the top of the banner with the folded flap toward the front. Staple the bottom frame in the same manner but without string. Hang up by the string.

RASCAL

Sterling North

Name _____

MOBILE MAGIC

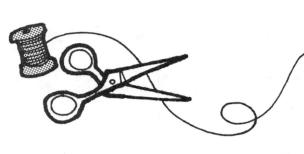

Create an exciting mobile to hang in your classroom.

Use string or fishing wire for hangers. Even a wire coat hanger can be used at the top.

Build down your mobile. Start by setting the scene at the top level, characters at the middle level, and developing the plot at the bottom level.

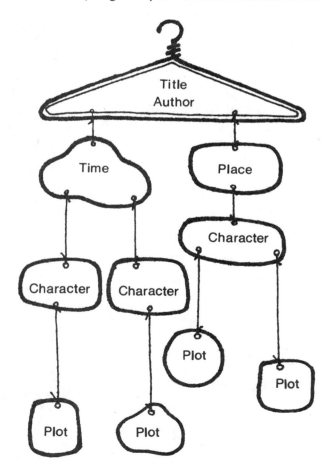

Be sure to put pictures on both sides so that, as the mobile moves in the breeze, the pictures can be seen from any direction.

After coloring in brightly with felt markers, hang up for an exciting addition to your classroom.

12

Name _____

PEEPHOLE BOX

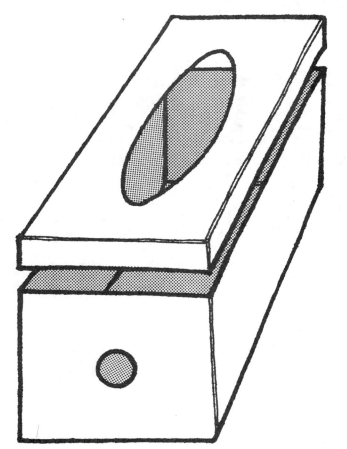

1. Take one shoe box.

2. Cut an oval hole in the top and a peephole in the end of the box.

3. Cover the outside of the top and bottom with white shelf paper, newspaper, gift wrap, etc., leaving holes open (optional).

4. Put the title, author's name and your name in bold letters on the top.

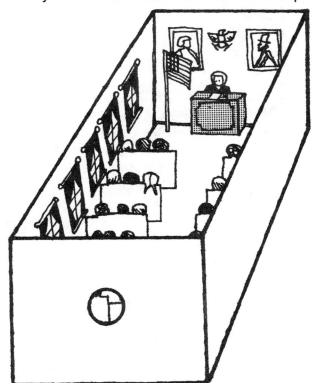

5. After deciding on the scene you wish to portray, cover the sides and bottom of the inside of the box to show the background scenery. Show details — clouds, birds, trees, bushes, drapes, view through windows, pictures on walls, fireplace. etc.

6. Construct small characters and props out of construction paper. Be sure to have a tab at the bottom so it can be attached to the box.

7. Your box will be more exciting if your figures overlap when you look through the peephole. It creates a three-dimensional effect.

8. In the courtroom scene shown here, the student make it look like lots of seats by drawing this picture and gluing down the tab.

13

Name _____

PUPPET PLAYHOUSE

Take one scene from
your book and develop
it into a puppet play.

1. Plan and write the dialogue
   of your play.

2. Cut open a box and use this
   pattern to make a stage.

3. Use one child's tube sock for each puppet.
Sew or glue on buttons for eyes and a nose.
Then glue on yarn for hair and felt or construction paper clothes. Use felt-tip pens to add
details.

4. Give a fantastic play!

14

Name _____

GHASTLY GALLERY

Read a descriptive passage about the main characters in your book. Write the basic points of that passage here:

_____

_____

_____

_____

Now draw a picture of that character in this frame:

Title: _____

Author: _____

Brief Summary: _____

_____

_____

Name _____

RECORDER INTERVIEW

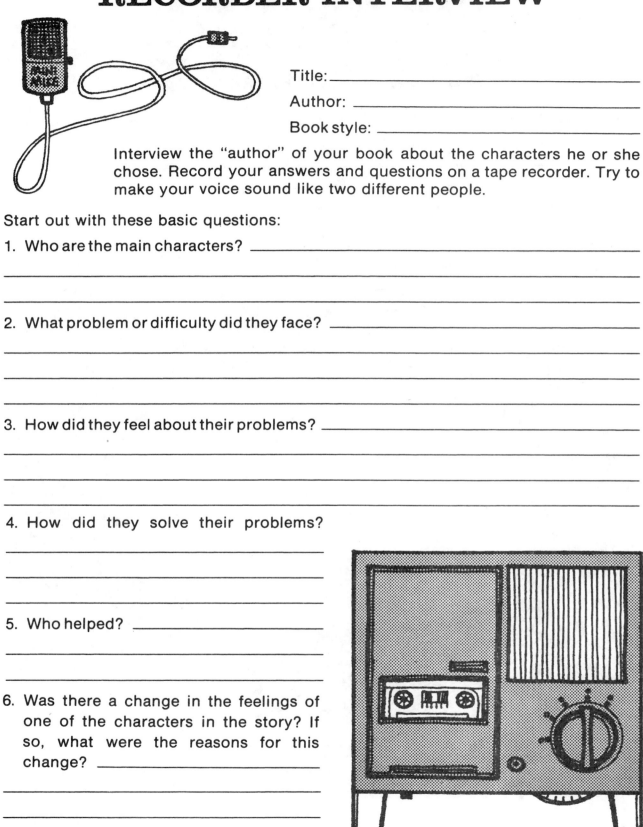

Title: _____

Author: _____

Book style: _____

Interview the "author" of your book about the characters he or she chose. Record your answers and questions on a tape recorder. Try to make your voice sound like two different people.

Start out with these basic questions:

1. Who are the main characters? _____
_____
_____

2. What problem or difficulty did they face? _____
_____
_____
_____

3. How did they feel about their problems? _____
_____
_____
_____

4. How did they solve their problems?
_____
_____
_____

5. Who helped? _____
_____
_____

6. Was there a change in the feelings of one of the characters in the story? If so, what were the reasons for this change? _____
_____
_____
_____

Name _____

SUPERHEROES

Schoolville Comics Presents

TITLE

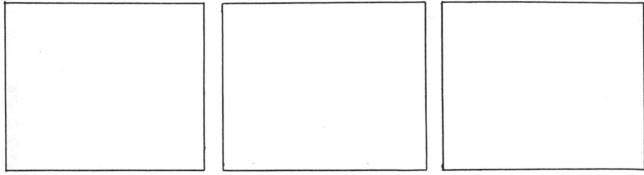

Turn your book's main character into a superhero by exaggerating his/her given characteristics in the book. Set the scene and fill in this comic strip.

17

Name _____

JIGSAW JOY

Title _____

Author _____

Draw a detailed picture of the main character(s) of your book in the box below. Show how the character(s) feel in your drawing, and include the title and author in the drawing. Color in the picture. Glue your paper to a piece of cardboard. Cut out your puzzle and place the pieces in an envelope or can for someone else to put together.

Name _____

THE PLOT PARADE

A parade is an orderly procession down the street, while a plot is an orderly procession through a book. See if you can follow the plot by answering these questions about your book.

1. Title _____
   Author _____
   Type of book _____

2. Introduction (How does the book begin?) _____
   _____
   _____

3. Crisis (What is the problem?)
   _____
   _____
   _____

4. Rising Action (How do the characters begin to solve the problem?)
   _____
   _____
   _____

5. Climax (What is the turning point of the story?)
   _____
   _____
   _____
   _____

6. Falling Action (How is the problem finally solved?)
   _____
   _____
   _____

7. Resolution (How does the story end?)
   _____
   _____
   _____

Name _____

GOT A GAME?

Title: _____

Author: _____

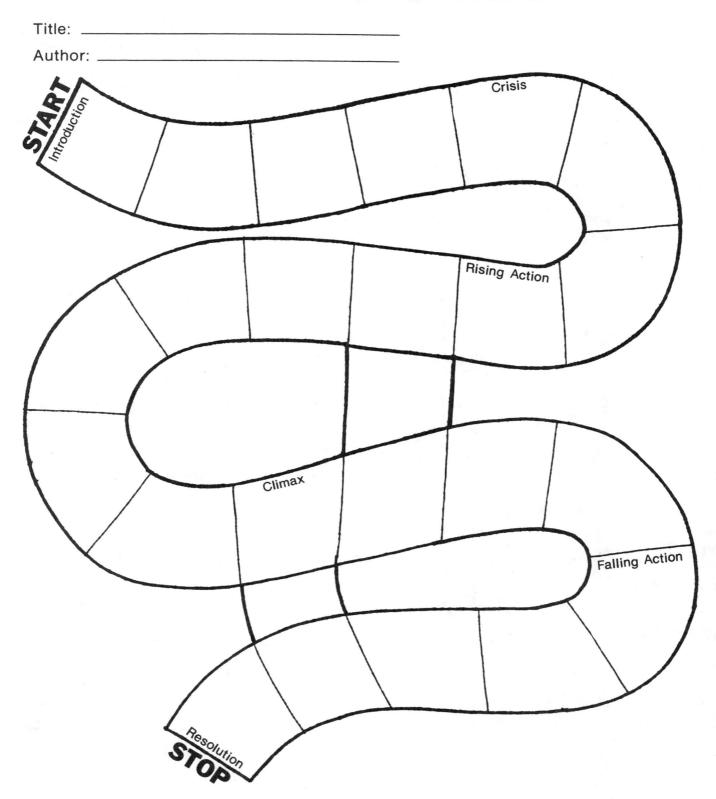

START — Introduction

Crisis

Rising Action

Climax

Falling Action

Resolution — STOP

Make your own game. Make game pieces to represent the main characters. Add illustrations to represent the scene. Set up directions, extra cards, and information on the spaces to follow the plot of your book.

PROGRAM THE COMPUTER

TITLE _____

AUTHOR _____

INPUT   OUTPUT

SETTING .... _____

TIME .... _____

CHARACTERS .... _____

                           _____

STORY INTRODUCTION .... _____

                           _____

CRISIS (PROBLEM) .... _____

                           _____

RISING ACTION .... _____
(WORK ON PROBLEM)

                           _____

CLIMAX .... _____
(TURNING POINT OF ACTION)

                           _____

FALLING ACTION .... _____
(SOLVING PROBLEM)

                           _____

RESOLUTION (ENDING) .... _____

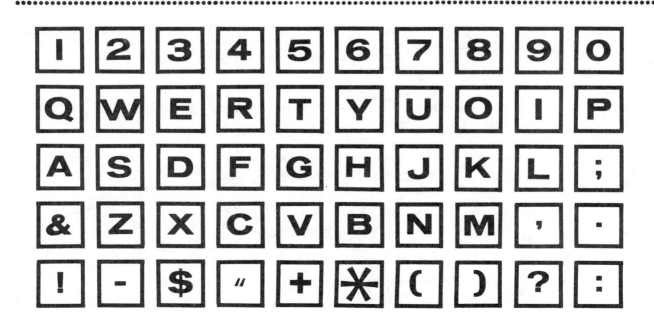

Name _____

TELEPHONE THE NEWS

817-225-0124

How well do you read for details?

Title _____

Author _____

1. Give the first and last names of three characters.

   _____

   _____

2. Tell where and when the story takes place.

   _____

   _____

   _____

3. Find sentences in the book that tell:

   — how something sounds _____

   _____

   — how something feels _____

   _____

   — how something smells _____

   _____

   — how something looks _____

   _____

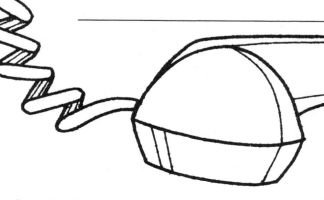

Name _____

AD APPEAL

Draw a poster to advertise your book. Make it **very** detailed to show the setting, being sure to depict at least one character and one major event in the book. Do **not** copy your picture, as it is to be your own interpretation. Be sure to include the title and author's name.

Name _____

BOOK JACKET JAMBOREE

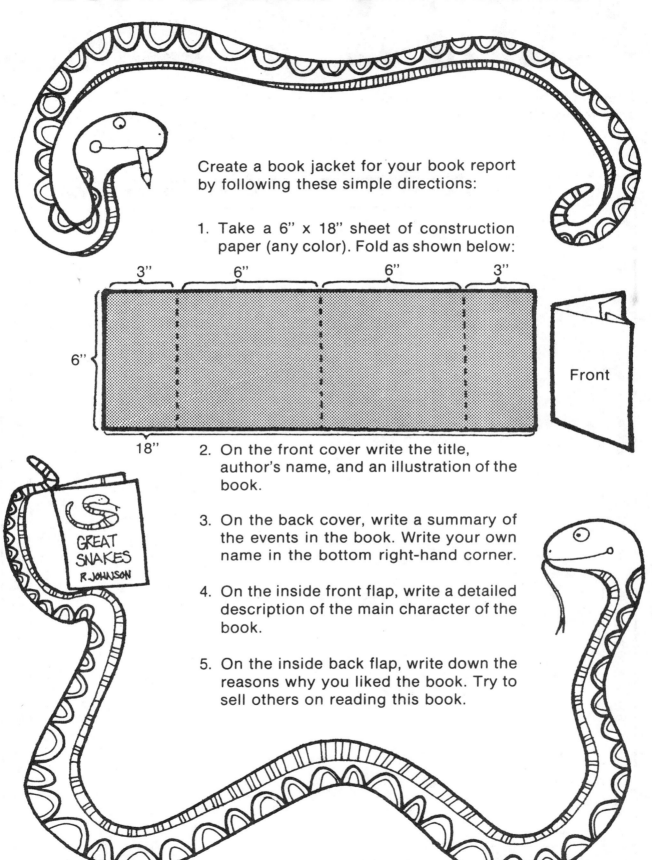

Create a book jacket for your book report by following these simple directions:

1. Take a 6" x 18" sheet of construction paper (any color). Fold as shown below:

Front

3" 6" 6" 3"

6"

18"

2. On the front cover write the title, author's name, and an illustration of the book.

3. On the back cover, write a summary of the events in the book. Write your own name in the bottom right-hand corner.

4. On the inside front flap, write a detailed description of the main character of the book.

5. On the inside back flap, write down the reasons why you liked the book. Try to sell others on reading this book.

GREAT SNAKES
R. JOHNSON

Name _____

FUN BOOK REPORT
PROJECTS

Now is the time to make a project book report. Choose the type of project that particularly appeals to you.

Try to make your project represent your book. For example:

Title of Book	Project
The Clue of the Brass-bound Trunk	Miniature trunk with clues
The Mystery of the Ivory Charm	Small elephant carved out of white soap, hung on a chain
The Bicycle Book	Bicycle made of toothpicks
The Borrowers	A miniature cloth banner

Here are some general project ideas:

Time-line poster
Information wheel
Soap carving
Wood carving (sign or plaque)
Balsa wood carving
Jigsaw puzzles (out of wood or cardboard)
Scrolls
Sample diary
Posters
Treasure maps
Paper mosaic illustrations
3-D pop-up pictures
Decoupage signs
Puppets
Mini-books
T.V. show
Shoe box filmstrip

Mini-mural
Shoe box diorama
Stuffed doll, characters
Cloth hanging, colored with textile crayons or felt markers
Set of paper dolls
Miniature cardboard scenes
Popsicle stick models
Appliqué or stitchery designs
Mystery clues in specially made containers that relate to book titles
Old-fashioned maps with burned edges
Clay or papier maché models
Slide show
Mobile

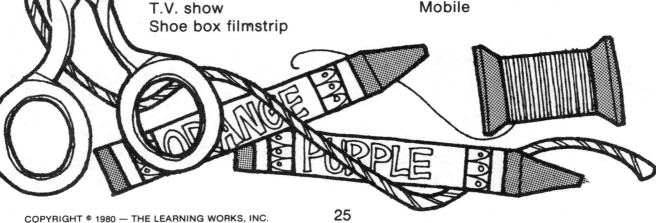

Name _____

SPINNING WHEEL

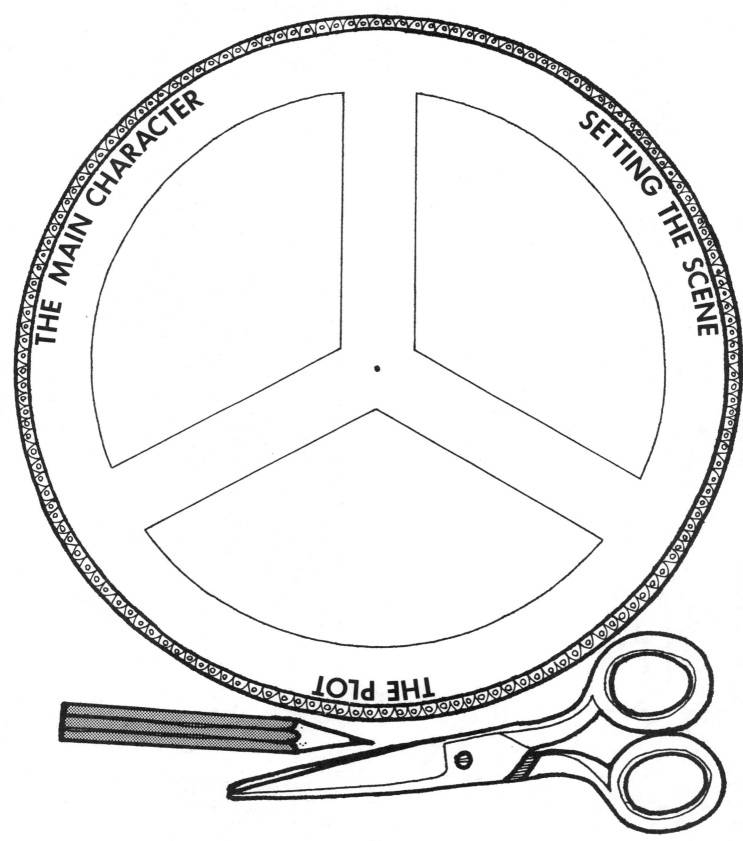

THE MAIN CHARACTER

SETTING THE SCENE

THE PLOT

Name _____

SPINNING WHEEL

Directions: On the large circle on page 26, write detailed descriptions of the scene, characters, and plot within the correct pie-shaped space.

On this small circle, write the title and author of the book and your name, and draw a simple illustration of your book.

Cut out both circles, and attach at the center with a brad.

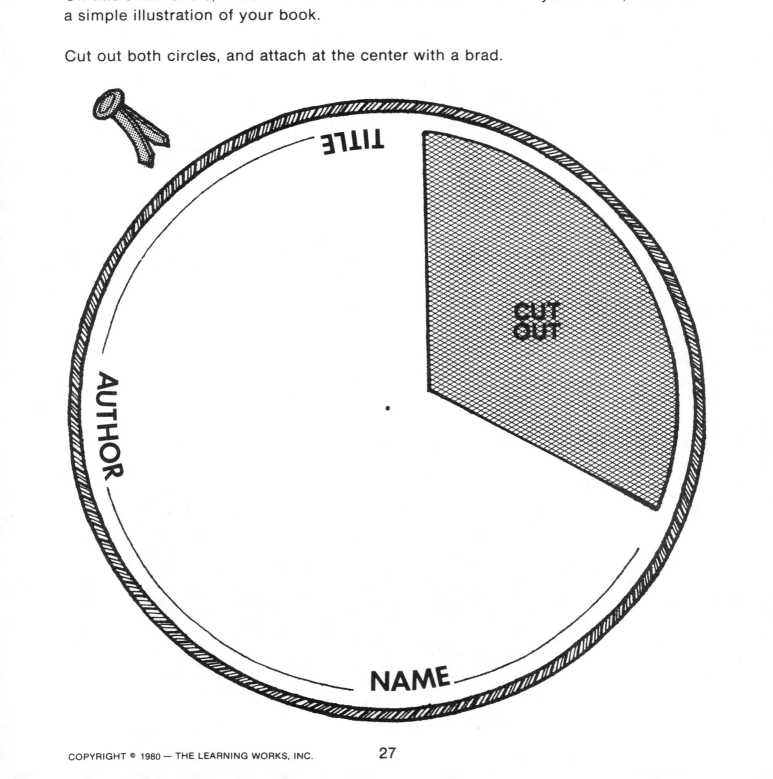

Name _____

NONFICTION

Title _____

Author _____

Publisher _____

Date Published _____ Call Number _____

RECREATION

MEDICINE

SPORTS

APPLIED SCIENCE

HISTORY

GEOGRAPHY

APPLIED ARTS

LANGUAGE

1. Why did you choose to read this book?

_____

_____

_____

_____

2. List ten interesting facts you learned from this book.

_____

_____

_____

_____

_____

_____

_____

_____

_____

_____

3. What makes this book different from others of its kind?

_____

_____

_____

_____

4. What is your opinion of this book? _____

_____

_____

_____

_____

_____

_____

POLITICS

PURE SCIENCE

GOVERNMENT

Name _____

WORLD OF SCIENCE

Title _____
Author _____

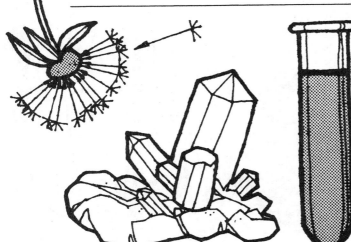

What area of science does this book cover? _____
_____
_____
_____
_____

Why did you choose this book? _____
_____
_____

List six interesting facts you learned from this book.
_____
_____
_____
_____
_____
_____

What was your opinion of this book? _____
_____

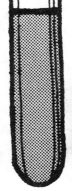

_____
_____
_____

Name _____

TRAVEL TALK

Read a book about a country, about geography, or about travel.

Title _____

Author _____

Topic _____

What did you like best about one of the places in your book? _____

_____

_____

_____

How is this place similar to where you live? How is it different? _____

_____

_____

_____

_____

Why would you like to live there? _____

_____

_____

_____

Why would you prefer to stay where you are? _____

_____

_____

_____

30

Name _____

SPORTS ILLUMINATED

Date _____

Issue #63

Title _____

Author _____

What sports were covered by this book?

_____

_____

_____

_____

_____

_____

Describe the sports hero about whom the book gave the most interesting information.

_____

_____

_____

_____

_____

_____

_____

_____

_____

_____

_____

What six sports facts did you learn?

_____

_____

_____

_____

_____

_____

_____

_____

_____

_____

_____

_____

_____

_____

Would you recommend this book to others? Why or why not?

_____

_____

_____

_____

_____

_____

_____

_____

Name _____

HOW TO DO IT HOBBIES

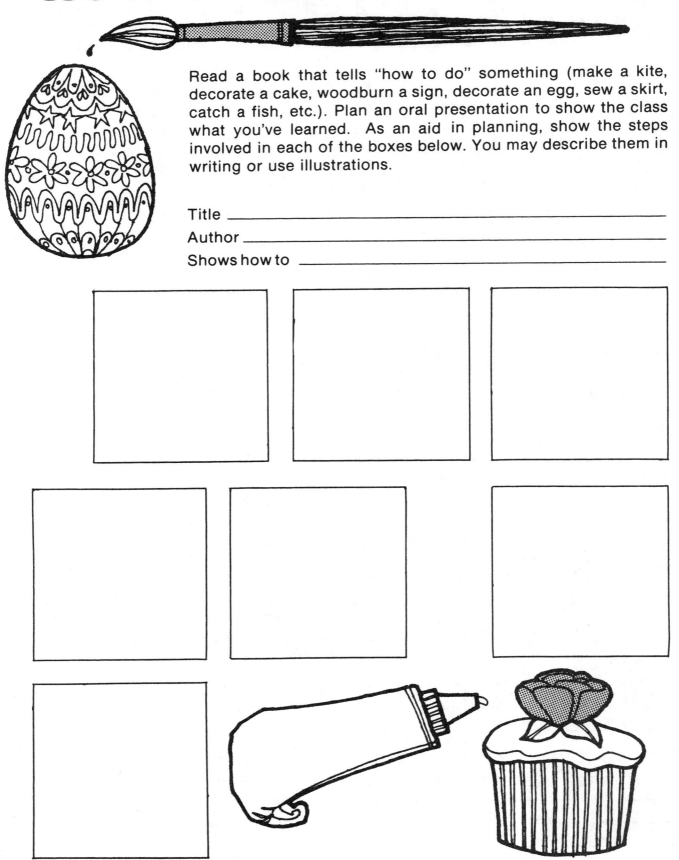

Read a book that tells "how to do" something (make a kite, decorate a cake, woodburn a sign, decorate an egg, sew a skirt, catch a fish, etc.). Plan an oral presentation to show the class what you've learned. As an aid in planning, show the steps involved in each of the boxes below. You may describe them in writing or use illustrations.

Title _____

Author _____

Shows how to _____

32

Name _____

BIOGRAPHY

Pick a biography or autobiography about a famous person.

Title _____

Author _____

Read the book carefully, trying to put yourself in the position of the main character.

Complete one of these activities:

1. Make a puppet dressed as your chosen famous person. Have your puppet introduce himself/ herself to the class and describe himself.

2. Dress up as your famous person. Introduce yourself to the class and spend several minutes telling about the important events that have occurred in your lifetime.

3. Make a shoebox filmstrip and a tape recording to go along with it to tell the story of your famous person's life.

Name _____

POETRY POTPOURRI

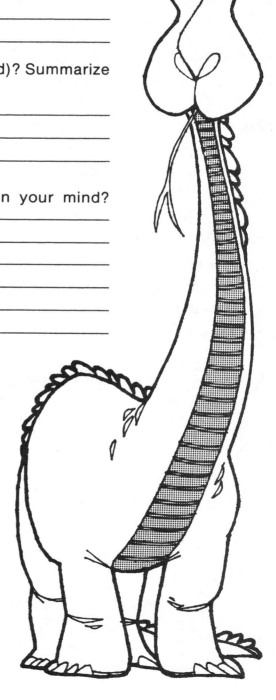

A. Read a collection of poems.

B. Choose your favorite poem from the book and answer the following questions:

1. Who is speaking in the poem? _____
    _____
    _____

2. Is there a story being told (narrative ballad)? Summarize the author's meaning.
    _____
    _____
    _____

3. Does the poem create strong images in your mind? What are they? _____
    _____
    _____
    _____
    _____
    _____

4. Does the author use rhyme, colorful words, or special meanings to convey the message? _____
    _____
    _____
    _____
    _____

C. Select one four-line poem with an A-B-A-B pattern (1st and 3rd lines rhyme, and 2nd and 4th lines rhyme). Write your poem on the back of this paper.

D. Memorize the poem you just wrote. Be prepared to recite it to the class.

Name _____

SHORT STORY SURVEY

Read an anthology (collection) of short stories and complete the following sections for three of your favorite stories. See if they contain the three basic features of short stories.

Title _____

Author _____

Give examples to show that the story was created by the **author's imagination**.

How did the author **entertain** you?

What **problem** was **solved** in the story?

Story #1: _____
_____
_____

Story #2: _____
_____
_____

Story #3: _____
_____
_____

Please use the other side of this paper to complete your answers.

Summarize your favorite short story: _____
_____
_____
_____
_____
_____

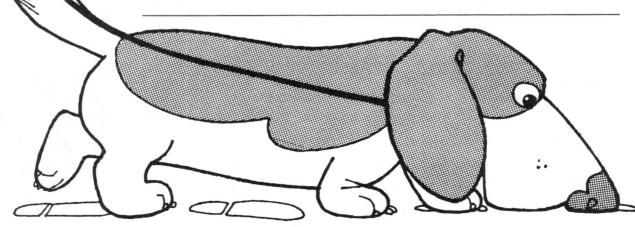

Name _____

SCI·FI

Science fiction stories usually transfer the characteristics of a present-day society to another time, often the future. The author must be creative in writing an imaginative story about this new and unknown place and time.

Read a science fiction book, and then answer the following questions in relation to your book.

Title _____

Author _____

Who is telling the story? _____
_____
_____
_____

In what kind of world is this story set? _____
_____
_____
_____
_____
_____
_____

What kind of problems did you find that were unique to this new world? _____
_____
_____
_____
_____

In what ways are the characters of this new world like us? . . . . different from us? _____
_____
_____
_____
_____

How is this book different from other kinds of books that you've read? _____
_____
_____

Name _____

WESTERN AND WILD

Many of the books about the Wild West tell the story of the "good guys" against the "bad guys". Describe the "good guys" and "bad guys" in your book and tell how they solved their problems.

_____
_____
_____
_____
_____
_____
_____
_____
_____
_____
_____
_____
_____
_____
_____
_____

Name _____

Dear: _____ ,

Title _____
Author _____
Period in history _____

Read a fiction book based on a period in history.
Write a letter from one of your book's characters to
a person who really lived during that time. Let the
letter reflect your character's attitudes toward his
or her life.

Name _____

Title _____

Author _____

CURIOUS CLUES

Cut on the dotted lines (— — — —) of each window. Then fold back on the solid line at the sides of each window. Glue a piece of paper behind each of the windows. Then, within each of the upper-floor windows, write a clue from your book. Finally, write the **solution** to the mystery in the first-floor window.

Name _____

ANIMAL FARM

There are three kinds of animal stories:

1. Animals who act like animals.

2. Animals who act like people.

3. Animals who act like animals, but talk like people.

Read a book with an animal story.

Title _____

Author _____

1. Which of the three types listed above is your book? _____

_____

_____

_____

2. Give two specific examples of how the animals in your book act. _____

_____

_____

_____

_____

3. Draw a picture or cartoon showing how the animals in your book act. Put your picture on the other side of this paper.

Name _____

"ONCE UPON A TIME"

"lived happily ever after" — and so begin and end most fairy tales.

Read a collection of fairy tales and give examples of how the authors included the following important fairy tale parts:

"Once upon a time" — _____
_____
_____
_____
_____
_____

Good and evil characters — _____
_____
_____

Magic or sorcery — _____
_____
_____
_____
_____
_____

Triplets (characters or events occurring in threes) — ____
_____
_____
_____
_____

"lived happily ever after" _____
_____
_____
_____
_____
_____

Title _____
Author _____

Name _____

Title _____

Author _____

The author of a tall tale ex-
aggerates all the major parts of
the story.

Read several tall tales and then
describe how the authors have
exaggerated:

"Babe carefully stepped over the barn and silo."

THE MAIN CHARACTERS: _____

_____
_____
_____
_____
_____

THE SETTINGS: _____

_____
_____
_____
_____
_____

EVERYDAY EVENTS: _____

_____
_____
_____
_____
_____

"Paul used a pine tree for a comb."

TALL TALES

Name _____

FAVORITE FABLES

Read a book of fables. Pick any four of the fables. For each one, write the moral (lesson taught) in the fable and then describe how the author developed that moral with the story characters.

1. _____
_____
_____
_____
_____

2. _____
_____
_____
_____
_____

3. _____
_____
_____
_____
_____

4. _____
_____
_____
_____
_____

Title _____
Author _____

Name _____

MYTHOLOGY

Read a book of myths.

Title _____

Author _____

Choose your
favorite myth to answer these questions:

1. What gods or heroes were main characters?
   _____
   _____

2. What super-abilities did these heroes have?
   _____
   _____
   _____

3. What major problem(s) confronted the main characters?
   _____
   _____
   _____
   _____

4. How were these problems resolved?
   _____
   _____
   _____
   _____
   _____

Name _____

ORAL REPORTS

Fill out your Information Plan:

Author:	Setting:
Title:	Kind of book:
Publisher:	Main characters:
Event 1:	Event 4:
Event 2:	Event 5:
Event 3:	Event 6:

Other kinds of oral reports that can be even more interesting are:

1. Act out a dialogue between two of your book's characters.

2. Act out an interview of the author or main character.

3. Act out one event from the book that shows the feelings of one of the characters.

4. Leave out the ending when you give your oral report and see if your classmates can guess the ending.

5. Orally read one exciting (and SHORT) passage from the book and then discuss how the author made it exciting.

Remember To:

1. Stand up tall and hold still.

2. Look at your audience.

3. Speak loudly and clearly.

4. Use an interesting voice.

5. Practice beforehand and relax. Time yourself.

6. Don't memorize your report. Use key notes to help you remember the order of the information.

Name _____

CLASSROOM CATALOG

Help set up a classroom catalog of short book reviews by filling in these file cards for each book you read.

File your cards alphabetically under the author's last name.

Author _____ Call # _____

Title _____

Type of book _____

Reviewer's Opinion/or Summary _____

_____

_____

_____

_____

_____

☐ Recommended
☐ Not Recommended _____

Reviewed by:

Author _____ Call # _____

Title _____

Type of book _____

Reviewer's Opinion/or Summary _____

_____

_____

_____

_____

_____

☐ Recommended
☐ Not Recommended _____

Reviewed by:

Author _____ Call # _____

Title _____

Type of book _____

Reviewer's Opinion/or Summary _____

_____

_____

_____

_____

_____

☐ Recommended
☐ Not Recommended _____

Reviewed by:

BOOK REPORT CHECKLIST

Student's name _____ Room _____

Date	Title	Author	Type of Book	Type of Book Report	Report Grade

SPUR
of the Moment
IDEAS

(for general type book reports)

Write a new ending for the story.

Write a diary entry by the main character describing a major event in the book.

Make a crossword or word find puzzle using words and characters from the book.

Make stand-up characters (popsicle stick backing) to illustrate the characters in the book.

Write a book review for a newspaper or magazine and send it for possible publication.

Make a clay, soap or wood model to illustrate a phase of the book.

Make a time line of events in the story.

Make a seed mosaic to illustrate part of the book.

Make a short radio play.

Make a shoebox filmstrip.

Make a flannelboard story.

Draw a cartoon strip of events.

Write questions you think everyone should be able to answer after reading the book.

Write some riddles about the story.

Compare (in writing) a character in the story with a real person you know. Tell how they are alike and different.

Write a letter recommending the book to a friend.

Write a note to the librarian suggesting why the book should be recommended to other students.

Make a diorama to represent a part of the story.

Prepare a newspaper based on the book.

Make a scroll.

Make a doll to represent a character.

Write an epilogue to the story.

Make a stitchery sampler.

Make an overhead transparency to accompany an oral report.

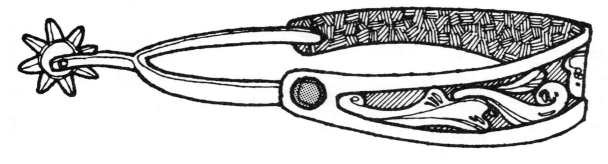